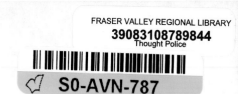
Thought
Police

Taylor Sapp

Alphabet Publishing

Contents

Before You Read

1. What does the term thought police mean?

2. Do you think technology will be able to read people's minds some day?

3. What are the advantages and drawbacks of being able to read people's minds?

4. Should people should be judged for their thoughts? Why or why not?

5. Should police monitor people that they think might do something wrong?

6. What kinds of acts are morally wrong but not illegal?

Thought Police

Travis was a member of the Thought Police. Today had started as just another day for him. But that's not how it would end.

Travis worked in the Thought Watching department of the Portland office of the Thought Police. His job was to scan the thoughts of people living in Sector J1B, the part of town where his office was located. The computer in front of him received thoughts from people in the area. It then filtered out any thoughts that were clearly not a problem. A lot of people were thinking about innocent things. Some people were remembering a shopping list. Others were making plans for the evening or worrying about a small problem at work. Others were singing a song in their head and so on. Normal things.

Travis' computer sent him the other stuff. A man who was angry at his boss, a teenager thinking about buying drugs, a woman who secretly hated her husband. His job was to listen to thoughts and note anyone who was planning to break the law. Then, Thought Police Officers would be sent to the target location. Their job was to stop crime before it happened by any means necessary.

Usually, when the person saw the police, they stopped planning anything bad. Sometimes the police had to get rough, though. In extreme cases, thought criminals were put in jail or even had their minds erased.

Now that police could read people's thoughts, it was easier to keep the peace. A lot of acts had become crimes. Angry or violent thoughts against the government was a new crime. This prevented acts of terrorism. Lying was also illegal in most cases. Lying made a society weak. Even adultery, or cheating on your spouse, was a crime now. It caused too much disorder.

• • • • • • • • • •

Travis had already alerted police about two people today. The first was for suicidal thoughts. Killing yourself took away a potential worker. The other one was big. A man who had just purchased a gun was having violent thoughts. Travis was feeling really good about his day. He'd prevented at least two deaths. Even if he didn't catch another offender, he'd already done a lot of good work. He was sure his boss, Noah, would be satisfied.

Suddenly a new thought scan came in. Travis listened in on the thought. It was a woman. She was having thoughts about a man who was not her husband. Travis recognized the woman's thought voice, even before her picture appeared on his monitor. It was Dina. They had gone to high school together.

There was a problem, though. The man Dina was thinking about was Travis!

Travis had a crush on her in middle school but he was too shy to ask her out. In high school, they were both on the debating team. And one day, she had asked him out! They had had a good relationship. They liked to go to coffee shops and talk about big ideas. They took a few camping trips together and got very close.

Travis had thought they would go to the same university, then get married, and have kids.

Unfortunately, in their junior year, Dina moved to Japan. Her father was a captain in the US Army and he was assigned to a military base near Tokyo. Travis and Dina tried to stay in touch but it was hard. She fell in love with Japan and decided to stay there for university. She met someone else and stopped answering Travis' letters.

They had seen each other one more time. Five years ago, there was a high school reunion. She was visiting the US and she had come. It was clear that they still had feelings for each other. They left the party early and spent the night in his apartment. Most of the time, they talked and laughed and shared good memories.

The next day, she went back to Japan. Soon after, they both got married. She married a Japanese doctor and he married a fellow police officer. He thought it was over with Dina. But now, he knew she was thinking of him. Travis was surprised and worried and confused.

First, he was surprised she was back in the US. He searched the police database quickly and got her record. She and her husband had moved back to the US last year. She had gotten a job offer at a big bank in town. The husband had no job. Maybe he was frustrated. Living in another country and having no job and no friends was hard. Perhaps their marriage was suffering too.

Second, he was surprised that he felt excited. His marriage was also suffering. He and his wife worked long hours. They never saw each other. At the beginning, they got along well. But now they were strangers. That could happen sometimes. Dina was an exciting opportunity.

Third, he was worried. As a thought watcher, he should turn on the camera. That would show him what she was doing. However, if he saw her, he might have illegal thoughts about her.

Finally, he was anxious about what to do. If he reported her, she could get in trouble. He cared about her, at least a little. If he didn't report her, he could get in trouble. What if his boss found out? He couldn't treat friends and family differently than other people!

Travis put his head in his hands and took a deep breath. Then he turned on the camera. There was Dina. She was looking at her old yearbook from high school. There was a picture in the yearbook of Dina and Travis together. They had their arms around each other and were smiling! Travis remembered that day. It was the morning after a big debate. Their team had won. Travis took Dina out for ice cream. She decided to play a joke on him. She ordered the Pig's Treat Ice Cream Sundae: 10 scoops of ice cream, 2 bananas, whipped cream, chocolate sauce and 4 kinds of sprinkles. Normally, 6 people would order it. The two of them finished it in an hour. They laughed the whole time. They got their clothes very messy. The next morning, he teased her, calling her a pig! She laughed. That's when the yearbook photographer took the picture.

Travis knew what Dina was thinking. He was thinking it too. What if she had never moved to Japan? What if they had gotten married? Travis quickly blocked his thoughts. They learned to do this in Thought Police training. Sometimes police had to think about hurting criminals. They had to hide these thoughts from the computer. Otherwise the system would be overloaded.

Before he could think more, Travis hit the green alert button, and closed the file. The police would now investigate. A green alert was the least serious level. It was Dina's first time. The police would probably remind her to keep her marriage strong. Then they would take her high school yearbook away. She might get one strike, at the worst.

Travis sighed and went to the break room to relax. His friend Quinn was there.

"Lacey and I had a big fight last night, but this morning she told me how much she loves me and how sorry she is! Crazy, huh? How are you and Shelby doing?" Quinn asked, fishing for the reason why Travis seemed confused.

Travis smiled. Quinn and his wife Lacey always had drama. They fought, they screamed at each other, they made up, they laughed together. At least their marriage was full of passion. It was very unlike Travis's marriage to Shelby.

"Same as always." Travis said. He and Shelby never fought. They never laughed either. All they talked about was household chores. Who would do the grocery shopping that week, who would go to the kid's soccer game, what to bring to a friend's party. It was all the usual stuff married couples had to talk about. Sometimes they talked about work. But Travis couldn't talk much about the thoughts he saw. It was illegal to share private thoughts outside the department.

Shelby worked a desk job. Her job was to do research about suspects and witnesses. Most of the time she was on the Internet or on the phone. So she didn't have a lot of exciting stories to share.

Quinn said, "Maybe you guys need to take a vacation. Take some time off. Go to Mexico together and relax on the beach. Have some fun as a couple."

"That sounds fun," Travis admitted. Then he thought about how Shelby would probably complain it was too hot. He would get burned by the sun and complain about that. They'd talk about what restaurant to eat at. Whether to go to the pool or the beach. When to get up for breakfast.

It was no use. He and Shelby were just bored together. If only...

His thoughts drifted back to Dina. He remembered that yearbook photo. How happy that had been. Everybody said they were perfect together.

"Travis, calm down." Quinn was studying his face. He knew something was wrong. He had worked in Thought Police for a long time.

The bracelet all citizens wore now suddenly flashed green. A warning. He had had illegal thoughts about Dina. The Thought Police was a Thought Criminal!

• • • ● • ● • • •

The police squad came to check on Travis. They were surprised that the criminal was a policeman himself. Quinn said he could take care of it.

"Hey, man!" Quinn said, "I don't know who you were thinking about. I don't care. You have to stop."

"What do I do?" Travis asked.

"You need to think about your marriage. Think about the good things about Shelby." Quinn said.

Travis looked doubtful. "OK, then try to focus on work."

Back at his computer, Travis got back to work as hard as he could. Luckily, he got a case immediately. There was a young man, S. Camus, who wanted to steal a watch from a shop. He clicked the button for a yellow alert. A yellow alert was more serious than green. The police would come with weapons. They would be ready to stop a crime.

The next hour was busy. A man was planning to walk away from a restaurant without paying. A policeman would walk by and stare at him. That would solve the problem.

A woman was thinking of taking her son to school and leaving them there. Police would investigate. Maybe she needed financial support. Maybe she needed to see a doctor. Travis hoped she would get the help that she needed.

There were more crimes. One man was having confused violent thought. Travis was proud to stop a potential serial killer before anything happened. People like that often needed serious help. In the worst cases, they had parts of their mind erased. They lost memories. Sometimes they forgot who they were. But the mind erasing program worked. After mind erasing, people never had the bad thoughts again. They couldn't have any bad thoughts ever!

Then, a repeat offender alert came across his screen. That meant someone had committed the same thought crime twice in the same day. Travis gasped when he saw the name: Dina! What should he do? He didn't want anything bad to happen to her. He was happy she was thinking of him.

Suddenly, his bracelet flashed red. His boss came in with an armed policeman behind him. Travis knew what was happening. His thoughts of Dina were too strong.

His boss said, "Travis, you need to come with us. We can't let the Thought Police commit Thought Crimes."

Travis swallowed and said, "I want my mind erased!"

• • • • • • • • • •

They took Travis to a room in the basement. They connected him to a machine. They put a metal bowl on his head. Then they told him to think all about Dina. He enjoyed the chance to remember her. She was so beautiful and smart and funny. He remembered all their happy times.

Then there was a loud noise. His head hurt for a second. It felt like he banged his head on a kitchen cabinet. Wait. What was he doing in this strange room?

A voice asked, "Do you remember your name?"

He said, "My name is Travis. I am a member of the Thought Police. I am happily married to Shelby Griswold."

The people in the mind erasing room smiled! Another successful procedure!

• • • ● • ● • • ·

A few days later, Travis saw a RED alert come through his terminal that gave him a very odd feeling.

"Dina S. Thoughts about other men."

The description said something about impure thoughts about an old high school classmate. It was the tenth time that week. He knew what to do: Mind Erasing. He pressed the proper alert button and continued working.

He started smiling. It was his wife's birthday tomorrow. He had made big plans. A nice dinner at her favorite restaurant. Then drinks and dancing. He loved her so much. He was lucky to have a happy marriage.

Glossary

adultery: cheating on your husband or wife with another person

alert: a warning about danger or a problem, often a siren or light or message

alerted: warned someone of danger or a problem

assigned: sent to work at a particular place or given a specific task at work

chores: regular tasks that are done to take care of the house such as cooking, shopping, and cleaning

crush: a strong romantic interest in another person

debating team: a school activity where students compete by arguing about a particular topic

drifted: (here) moved or changed randomly

filtered out: removed unwanted things using a
tool of some kind.

frustrated: upset because something is hard to
do

gasped: breathed out air quickly in surprise or
excitement

high school reunion: an event where people re-
turn to their secondary school for a party

impure: (here) breaking moral rules

scan: to watch or listen to in order to get particular information

spouse: a husband or wife

suicidal: wanting to kill yourself

yearbook: a book published at schools every
year with pictures and descriptions of the year's
events

After You Read

1. What is the Thought Police?

2. What is Travis' job?

3. What kinds of things are thought crimes in the story? Were you surprised by any of the thought crimes?

4. Who is Dina? What is her relationship with Travis?

5. Where did Travis and Dina meet?

6. How did they break up?

7. Why did Dina think about Travis?

8. What is Travis' relationship with his wife like?

9. How did Travis get in trouble with the Thought Police?

10. What happens to Travis in the end?

11. Do you think this is a happy ending?

12. Do you think thought police could make the world safer?

13. Do you think mind reading technology will ever be real? Do you think it should be used the way it is in the story?

14. Should thinking about people outside your marriage be a crime?

Writing

1. If you could rewrite the ending, would you change it? How would you rewrite it?

2. What happens next?

- Does Travis commit another thought-crime?

- Does his marriage continue happily or not?

More Readers

Baby Shopping
Changes
Empathy
English Class on Mars
Ghost in My Room
Magic Employment Agency
Rebirth
Attack of the Sleep Demon
The AI Therapist
Thought Police
Time Travel Research: Genghis Khan
Virtual Unreality

AlphabetPublish.com/Book-Category/
Graded-Reader